Purr-fect Shiatsu

PURR-FECT SHIATSU

Tender Touches for the 90's Cat

BY JEFFREY RANBOM
ILLUSTRATED & DESIGNED BY DARRREN CHING

Intercultural Group, Inc.

First edition, 1993

Published by Intercultural Group, Inc.
10 East 23rd Street, Suite #600
New York, NY 10010

Editorial coordination in Japan by Shupan Kyoku

Printed in the U.S.A. on recycled paper.

Library of Congress Cataloging-in-Publication Data
Ranbom, Jeffrey.
Purr-fect shiatsu / by Jeffrey Ranbom; illustrated by Darren Ching.
p. cm.
ISBN 1-881267-07-5. $9.95
1. Cats—Diseases—Alternative treatment. 2. Acupressure for animals. 3. Cats—Health.
I. Title.
SF985.R36 1993
636.8'0895822—dc20

93-39127
CIP

ACKNOWLEDGMENTS

Special Thanks to:

Mr. Hirotoshi Narikawa, a shiatsu *practitioner in Tokyo, Japan, whose notebooks have helped in the preparation of the manuscript. Having provided* shiatsu *to his cats for many years, Mr. Narikawa brought to our attention how his healing work also provides quality time for himself with his pets.*

Sheppard for discussing how to corner cats on paper.

Marita Seaberg for reviewing drafts of the manuscript and mediating across cultural barriers.

Author's note: Do not try to diagnose or treat a feline health problem without consulting a qualified veterinarian. Consult a professional for your cat's needs before applying any recommendations provided in this book.

Table of Contents

Beginner's Mind
8

Introduction
Whither Shiatsu?
12

Chapter I
The Tao of Shiatsu
15

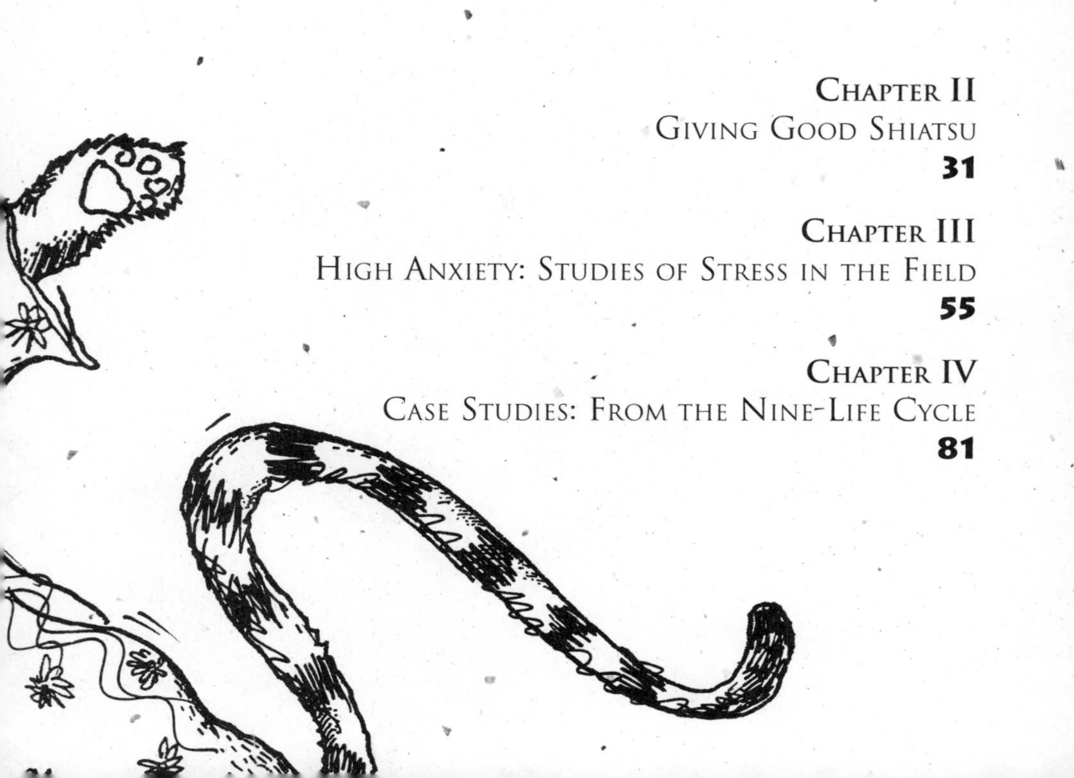

Chapter II
Giving Good Shiatsu
31

Chapter III
High Anxiety: Studies of Stress in the Field
55

Chapter IV
Case Studies: From the Nine-Life Cycle
81

BEGINNER'S MIND

When I accepted this assignment to write the first book on *shiatsu* for cats, I neither owned a cat nor practiced any of the healing arts. I was merely eager to embark on a thoughtful journey of discovery. I must have enjoyed what a Zen master might call "Beginner's Mind." Practitioners burdened with belief and years of training would probably never attempt to interpret complex materials for the uninitiated.

Of course, I did have second thoughts. *Shiatsu*, an ancient Asian healing practice performed with pressure of the fingers on various points of the body, has been regarded with skepticism by the medical establishment. Without the proper credentials and research skills, I might have invited further doubts from conventional caregivers about its effectiveness. And cat lovers worldwide are a more powerful audience than doctors.

After exhausting months of observation, I have gained enough expertise to realize that *shiatsu* and cats are mysterious and wonderful works of nature.

I wanted to inject a dose of humor to a high-minded body of medical literature. And I freely admit that since no compelling literature exists as to the evolution of *shiatsu*, I created my own historical artifact, the Yangtze Scrolls. Taking the form of a dialogue between a wise cat and an inexperienced student, this fiction seems very close to what should have taken place.

I leave it to the reader to determine the validity of this postcard from the edge of the new century.

Jeffrey Ranbom
New York, New York
October 1993

Introduction

WHITHER SHIATSU?

Through *shiatsu* we heighten our natural healing power to improve health and well-being. It is preventative in nature, can be practiced daily at little or no cost and addresses the common maladies of the total being—body and mind and spirit.

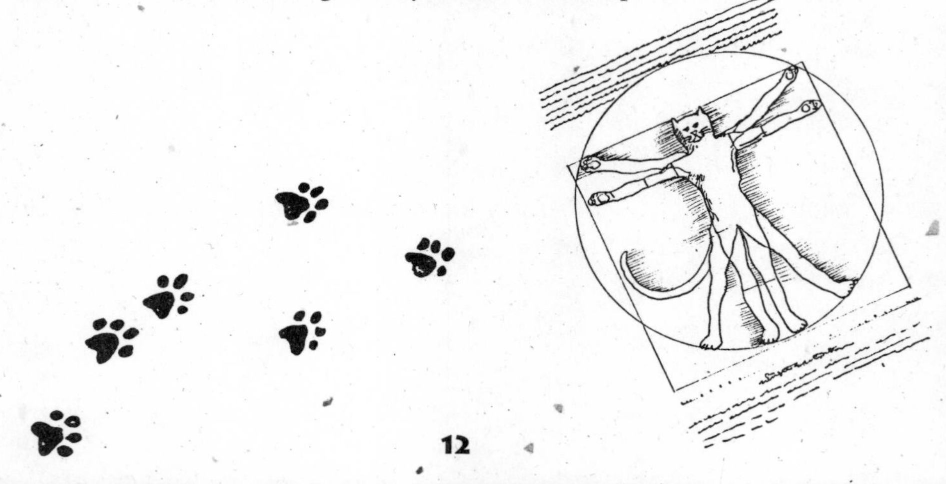

While humans can schedule a *shiatsu* massage to ease their aches and pains and find relief from the unhealthy stress of modern life, cats cannot make appointments. Cats do not complain about problems as loudly as their owners.

Cats, however, can gain the same benefits from *shiatsu* as their human companions. Do they deserve less? We are made up of the same stuff—*qi*—the energy of the universe.

We must preserve and protect our cats. Though they are proud and independent, we share adventures in domesticity. As the world outside sheds its mystery, our cats take us back to the wilderness.

Chapter I
The Tao of Shiatsu

HIGHWAY TO HEALTH

It is essential in any discussion of *shiatsu* for cats to consider the energy map of the universe. *Shiatsu* recognizes the importance of helping our cats to rediscover the rhythms of nature, finding a delicate balance of energies.

According to traditional Chinese philosophy and medicine, energy makes up everything in the universe, from a thought to the paper of this book. This vital energy, known as *qi* (and pronounced chee) is influenced by the dynamics of *yin* and *yang*, interrelated and opposing forces. When *qi* is in balance, body, mind and spirit enjoy a natural harmony that may even help us resist illness.

Energy races through the body of all living things along pathways called *meridians*. These routes are linked together like streets in a vast metropolis. The practice of *shiatsu* regulates the flow of traffic when gridlock occurs. When the flow of *qi* in the body is blocked or stalled, pressure is applied at critical intersections along the *meridians* called *tsubos*. The goal is to restore traffic to an uninhibited pace.

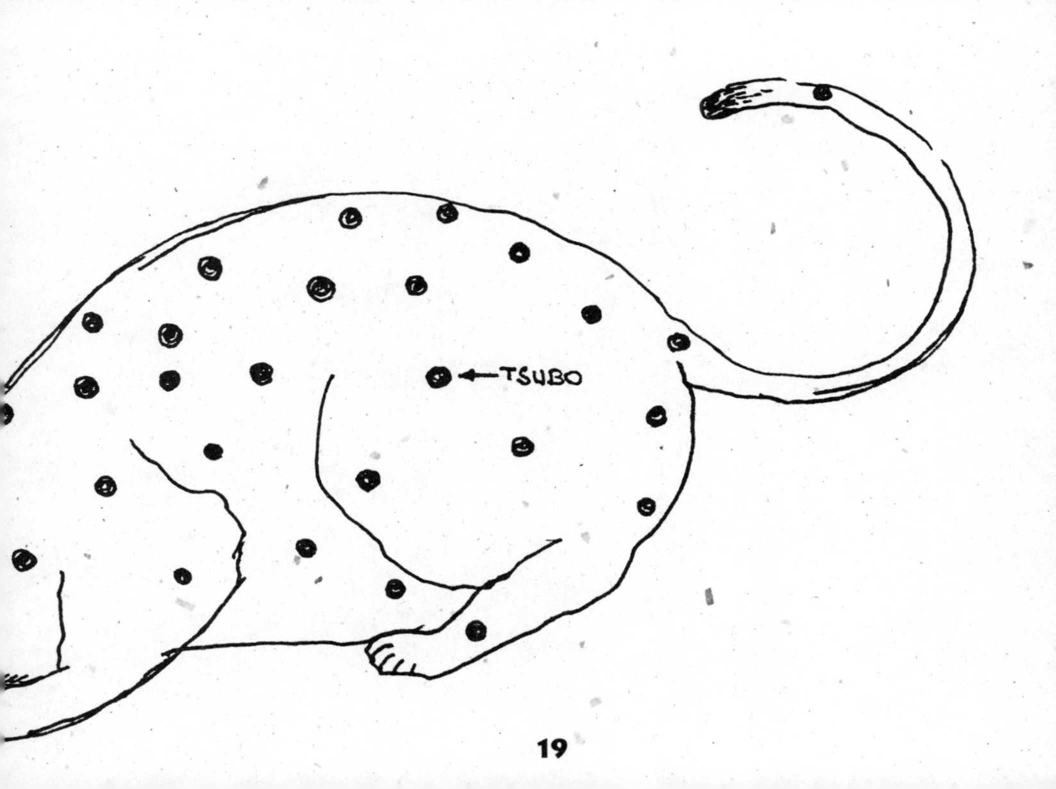
TSUBO

A BRIEF HISTORY OF QI

The following story of a cat and his disciple traces the history of shiatsu *to its origins in China and reveals that the future of both species was written in prehistory. Nearly four thousand years ago in the palace of The Yellow Emperor, a humble medical student named Shia Tsu was summoned to care for the emperor's cat, named Qi, who was preparing for his release to a tenth life.*

Shia Tsu: Master, you are ancient and wise. You must realize that I am not trained to prepare you for your journey. Surely there is a senior physician in the court, one who can attend your body, mind and spirit.
Qi: Why do you study within these gates? These doctors can only teach you how to set fees, not to care for patients.
Shia Tsu: Can you show me the way to happiness and longevity, so I may ease the suffering of men?
Qi: I will teach you to live according to nature through the practice of acupressure massage. My future rests in younger hands. Your hands.

Qi and Shia Tsu left the palace for a life of study in the hills along the Yangtze River. For two years, they worked daily from sunrise to sunset, speaking an obscure form of Chinese. They scratched a record of their conversations into linen books that they stored in earthenware pots.

When the scrolls were completed, Shia Tsu returned to the palace to take his place as the private physician of the emperor and the founder of Chinese medicine. Qi was released to the heavens where he became pure energy, shining like a constellation in the night sky.

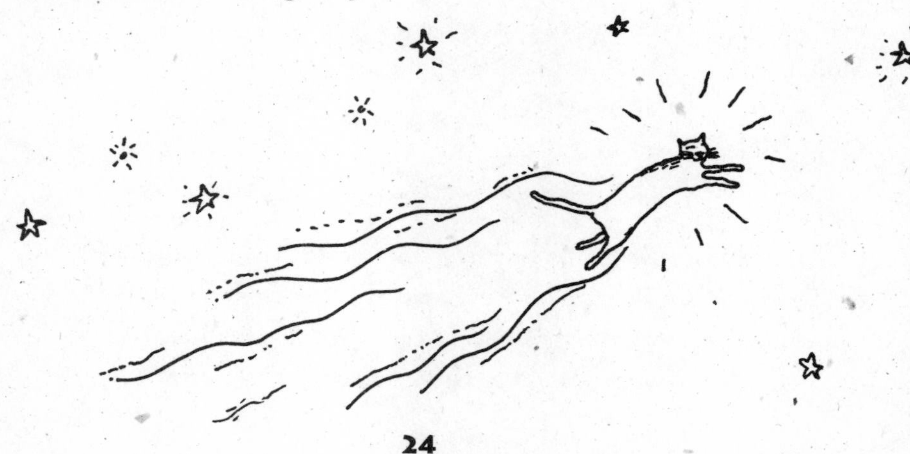

THE PHYSICIAN IN SPITE OF HIMSELF

In a fragment of the first scroll, Qi discusses critical aspects of the healing magic of acupressure massage.

Qi: Place both hands on my spine. Relax the thumbs and the fingers. One hand will be used for support; the other for manipulation.
Shia Tsu: I am a foolish boy. How will I know to do the right thing?
Qi: If your heart is pure, your intuition will guide you.
Shia Tsu: I am dizzy with dreaming. I will lose my grip.

Qi: Keep the pressure steady and firm. With your hands, trace the life-energy coursing through my body.

Shia Tsu: What if I rub you the wrong way?

Qi: The points will be revealed.

Shia Tsu: One hand knows not what the other is doing.

Qi: You have opened the gates, Shia Tsu. Do you feel the echo of life?

Shia Tsu: I cannot control it.

Qi: Practice. And you will find the way of healing.

Fifty years ago, Tsu Bo, a Buddhist cat carrying a staff, a notebook and an empty rice bowl—all of his worldly possessions—wandered from place to place like the scudding leaves of autumn. Though he begged for food and shelter during his pilgrimage, his days were filled with joyous adventure and reflection.

One day along the foothills of the Yangtze River where children and flowers blossomed, he followed a whim into an abandoned cave. Calling the place "House of Discovery," he built a fire in order to write poems in praise of Buddha. As the firelight intensified, a sparely furnished shelter came into view that exceeded his wildest dreams for a hermitage. His faith was further rewarded when he stumbled across a bank of earthenware pots that housed a treasure, the writings of Shia Tsu and Qi. Ever since Tsu Bo reported the discovery to scholars, the world has known these manuscripts as The Yangtze Scrolls.

The texts, surviving in pieces no larger than postage stamps, are the oldest medical books in the world. (Radio carbon dating has confirmed their antiquity from the twentieth century BC.) Only by an effort of imagination and years of painstaking reconstruction have we come to understand the meaning of the texts.

Acupressure massage, of course, is known today as *shiatsu* after the man who discovered its healing properties and promoted its practice. Pressure points along the *meridians* of the body are called *tsubos* in recognition of the monk who found a treasure of the lost scrolls. And the life energy of heaven and earth is called *qi*, a lasting tribute to a curious and crafty cat.

Chapter II
Giving Good Shiatsu

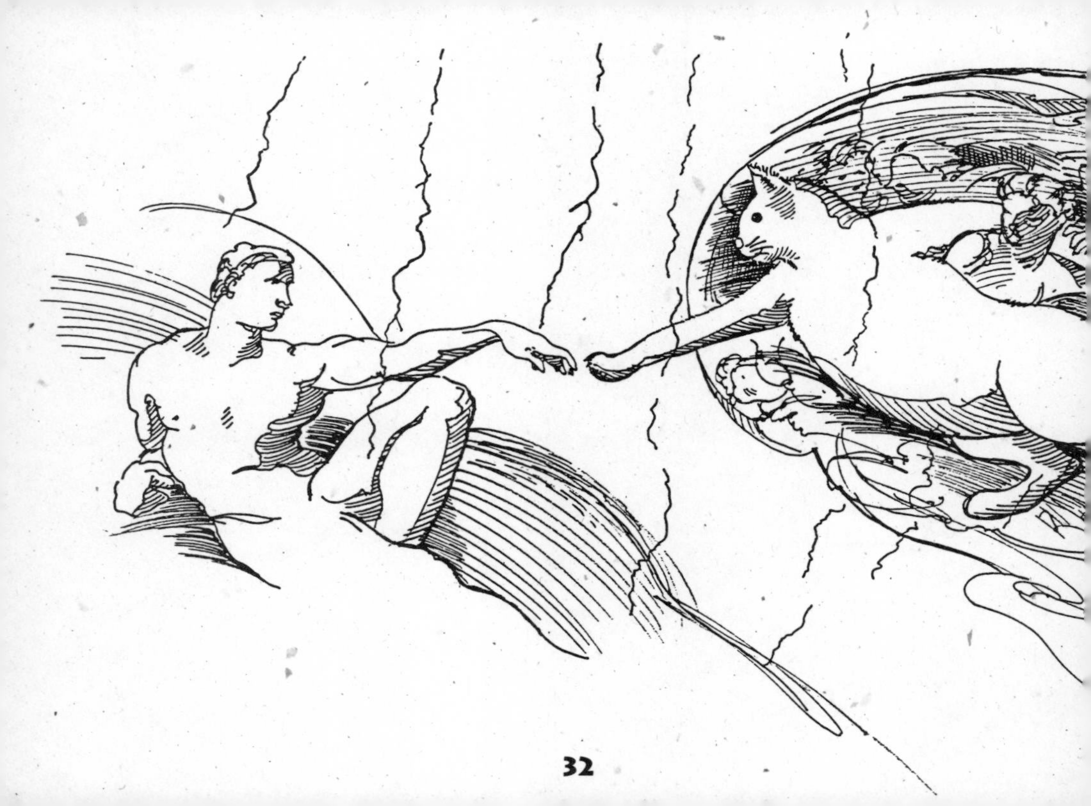

THE AGONY AND THE ECSTASY

The *shiatsu* artist, like Michelangelo, must have an intuitive understanding of the pressures of the age. He must also ply the tools of his craft, his heart and hands and inspired vision, in sculpting the cat. Our discussion now turns to explore how to deliver your cat from the agony of tension to the ecstasy of relaxation through *shiatsu*.

In our innocent infancy, we respected the power of gravity and the natural cycles of this turning earth. Didn't we spend months crawling before we learned to walk? To give good *shiatsu*, the practitioner must be grounded on the planet to convey to the cat that the process of massage is a natural one.

Below are exercises that will give you a healthy new perspective on the primal world.

Practice bowing to your cat. You will signal your respect to a higher authority.

Assume "the cat positions" of yoga. Once you're comfortable on all fours, crumple your college diploma into a ball and chase it around the room.

THE READINESS IS ALL

The *shiatsu* artist must remain in a constant state of calm readiness. Practice the following exercise for at least an hour a day.

Under My Thumb. Enhance your endurance. Inhale deeply. Then press with your thumb the remote control of the television. Change channels and volume fifty times every fifteen seconds. Exhale. Repeat.

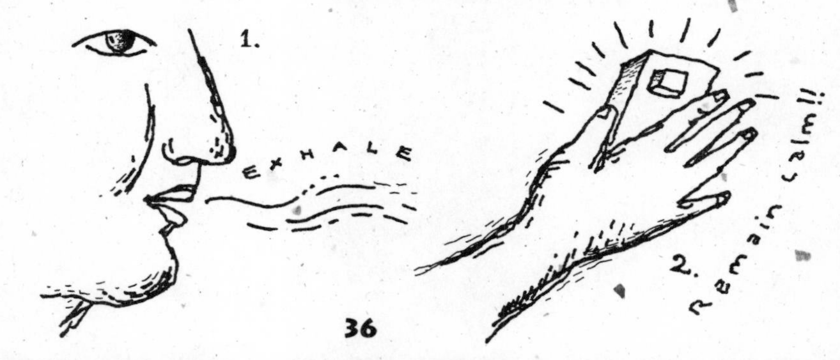

HOLD THAT TIGER

You are probably wondering by now how you are going to convince your cat to sit still long enough for a *shiatsu.* Approximately nine out of ten cats enjoy *shiatsu* to the extent that they will come to your side in anticipation of a daily session. Your cat may purr expectantly or direct your hand to the area where a massage would be welcome. For the reluctant ten percent, here are a few tips to encourage participation.

Hypnotism. Place lint on a silver chain and dangle it in alternate directions directly in front of your cat's eyes. Suggest repeatedly: "you are getting *shiatsu*, you are getting *shiatsu.*"

Drugs. Offer over-the-counter treats like catnip. Do not overdose. Watch for thwacking tails and narrowing eyes.

Psychology. Offer kitty a daily bath instead of *shiatsu*. Your cat will eagerly consent to *shiatsu*.

Shiatsu can be practiced anywhere there is an open space, from a stretch of carpet to a patch of grass. Before you begin, please consider these additional words of caution:

1. To avoid the chiropractor, the caregiver should perform *shiatsu* on a raised surface, like an ironing board. (No starch, please.)

2. Trim your nails.

3. Leave your worries in the old kit bag. Replaying in your mind the details of a recent audit will not help you concentrate on your cat's needs. Why not take a moment before a treatment to practice origami? Making paper tigers will help you better understand the form of the cat.

SHIATSU, ANYONE?

Let us now turn our discussion to the practical process of giving your cat good *shiatsu*. The pressure points along the *meridians* should not be massaged too strongly or without forethought. Gently increase pressure slightly only when it feels good to your cat.

Locating and stimulating specific *tsubos* is work for a specialist. It is sufficient for you to massage the area around the *tsubo* in a relaxed manner. You will gradually recognize the acupressure points as your fingertips become more sensitive and intuitively locate a blockage or an area of *qi* imbalance.

While it is not always easy to tell if your cat experiences pain or pleasure, purring is one sure indication that you are welcome to continue. Every cat has a favorite spot. With practice you will find it. Cats also have spots that you are not allowed to touch. It is advised that you never massage your cat's legs, heels or ribs without your cat's express written consent. Try not to do anything your cat doesn't like.

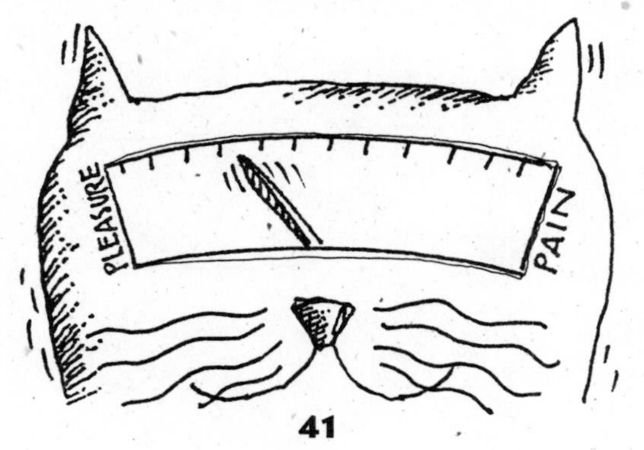

Ask your cat if she has had a hard day. If you empathize with the type and level of stress that your cat is feeling during the time that you were away, you will most effectively relieve her tension through *shiatsu*. You will also have an early report on damage or additions (like mouse presents) to your home. Always insure your residence against any acts of cat.

Hug your cat. Reassure her of your love and devotion. In Japan, *shiatsu* therapy and treatment are both often referred to with the same expression—*te-ate*—meaning *to apply a hand*. A warm hand radiating love during a massage can condition the *qi* energy flowing in your cat's body and deliver a healing effect. The *tsubo* located at the center of one's palm is the point from which *qi* is emitted, so when you gently touch your cat, you are making a *qi* connection.

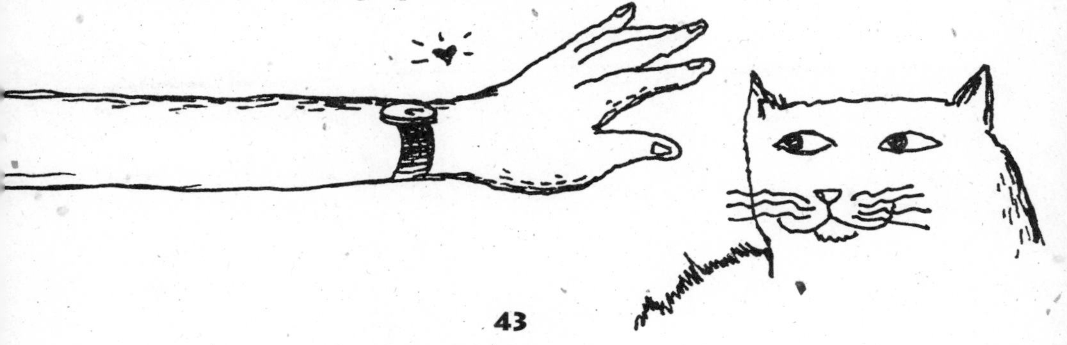

Stroke your cat's face. Cats really enjoy a facial massage. See if your cat enjoys a massage to the *tsubos* on the bridge of the nose. If so, gently press the point. Also try *shiatsu* on *tsubos* at the temples, both sides of the nose (especially when the nose is dry), above the eyes and along the eyebrows.

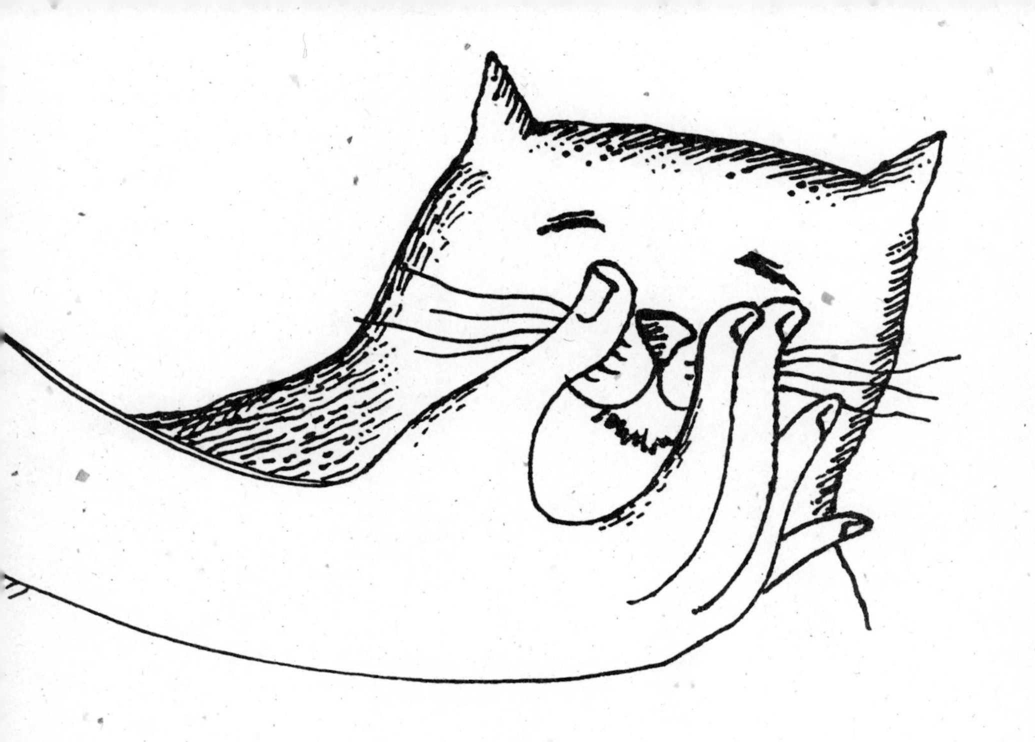

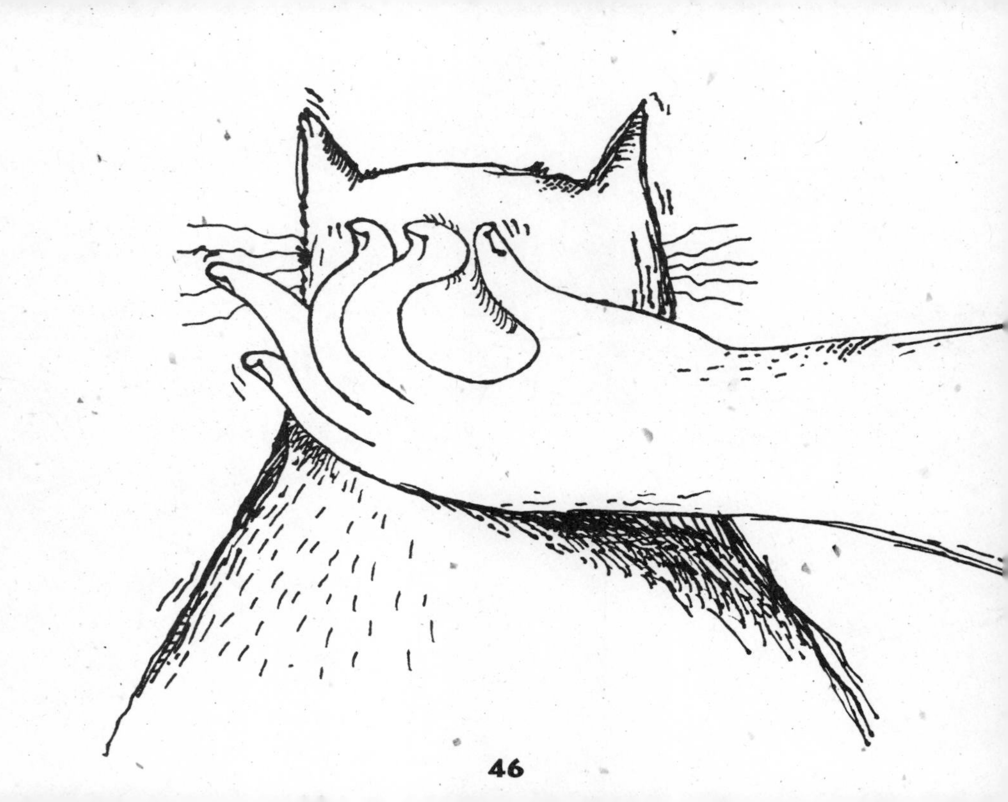

Massage your cat's neck.

The neck is the best spot to relieve muscle tension. With a light pinching action of your thumb and index finger, apply firm yet gentle pressure to the muscles on both sides of the cat's neck.

Massage your cat's back.

Tsubos located along the spine are related to the internal organs (liver, heart, kidney, lungs, etc.). *Meridians* connecting all *tsubo*s can be traced here, so by stimulating these points you can improve the flow of *qi* in your cat's entire body. If your cat is lethargic and you revitalize the flow of *qi*, your cat will perk up like Popeye after a helping of spinach.

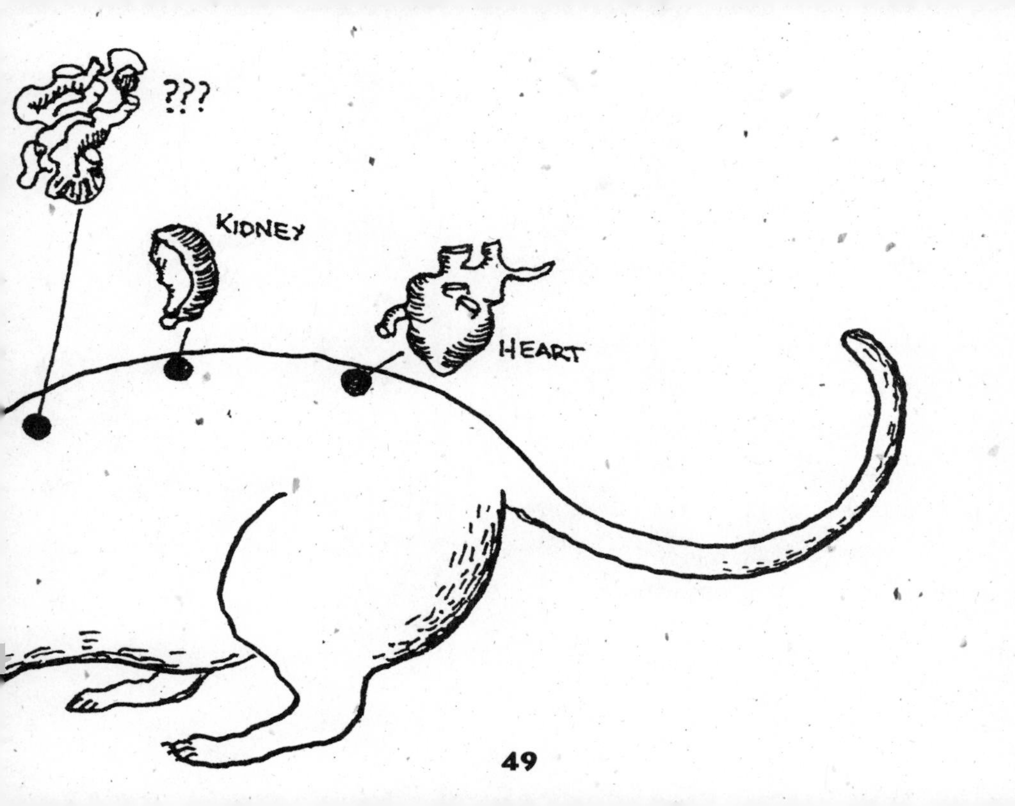
???
KIDNEY
HEART

If you rub both sides of the vertebrae, you'll find that there are two bony protrusions on each side. Begin just below the neck. The vertebrae of an healthy cat has a buoyant resistance to the touch. Pinch lightly between each protrusion. You may feel the blockages of *qi* along the *meridians* which feel convex or slightly hard to the touch. Press these *tsubos* firmly.

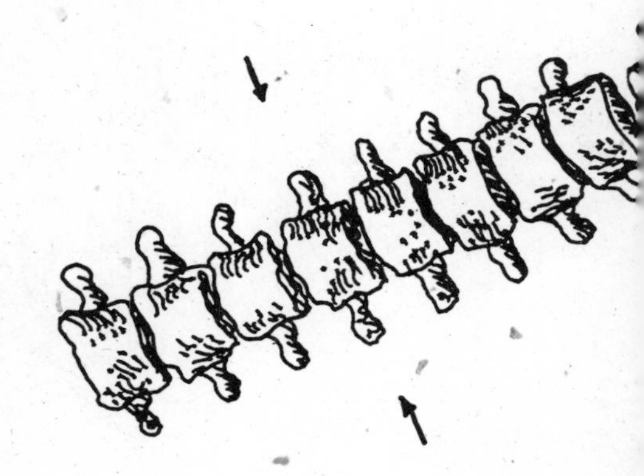

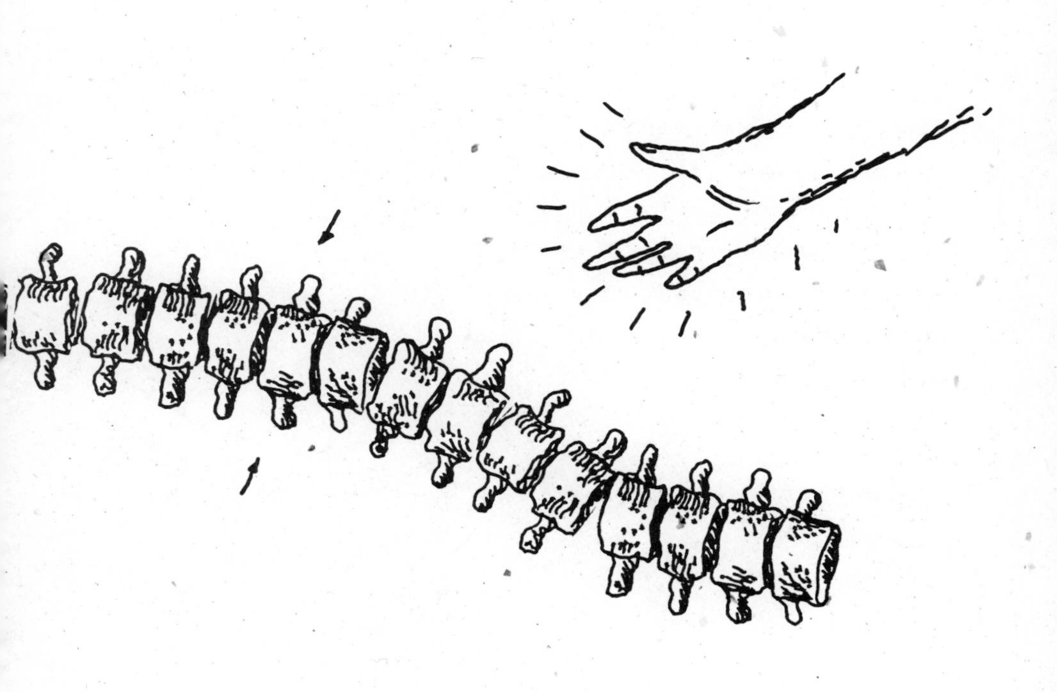

Massage your cat's stomach. Many cat's enjoy a stomach massage. Rub below your cat's ribs with your thumb. Then rub the abdomen very gently with your palm in a circular direction at the rate of one circle per three seconds. Watch for your cat's reaction. Massage with your fingers along a straight line down the center of the abdomen to relieve stomach ailments.

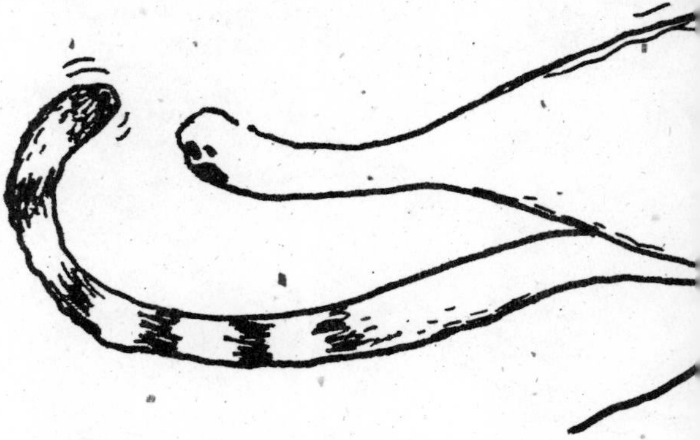

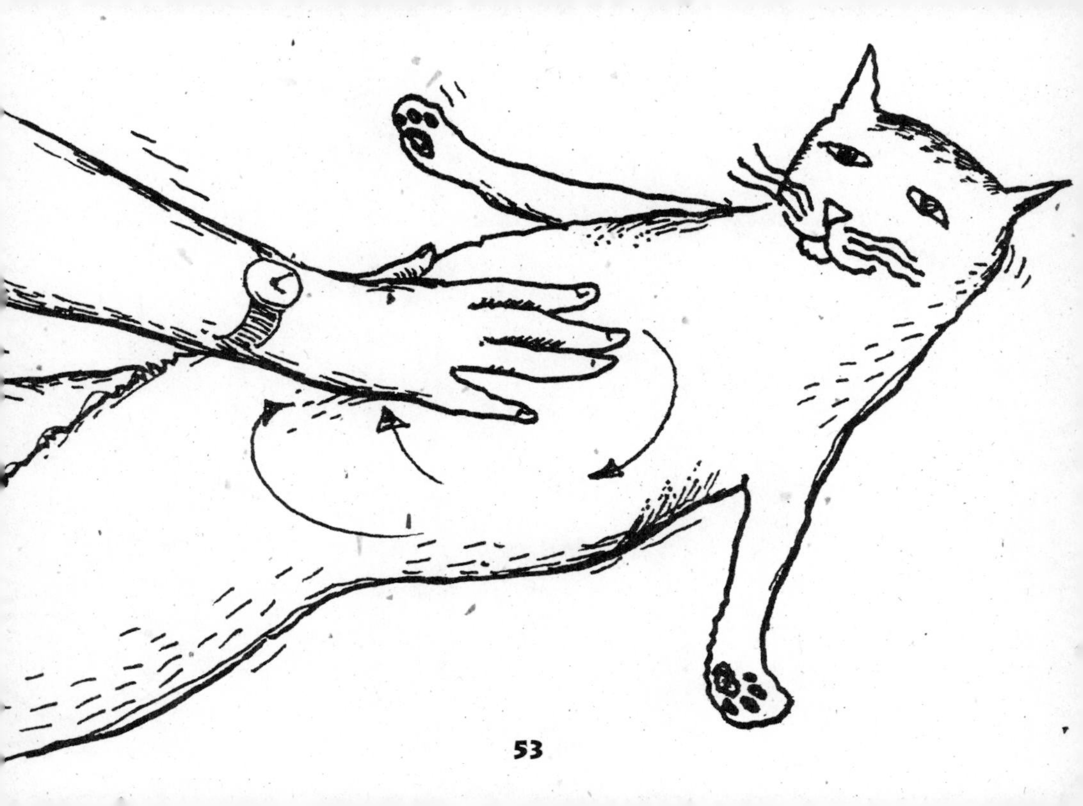

Chapter III
High Anxiety: Studies of Stress in the Field

SIX DEGREES OF EXASPERATION

Cats are generally subtle communicators who demand loving attention from their owners. How often have you lounged at breakfast, reading *The Times* with your coffee, when a cat will gently tap your newspaper, demanding a place on your lap and a session of admiration? How many times has a cat climbed into your bed and removed the sheet to signal the start of a new day together? There are stressful situations, however, that may arise within the home that will lead cats to more desperate forms of expression.

It is impossible to fully recognize what is going on around us amid the smoke and stir of the modern world. Nevertheless, it is essential that you have a thorough understanding of the stress that affects your cat in order to provide relaxing relief through *shiatsu*.

The following symptoms are but a few of the actions that your cat may take to cry for help:

Hiding. Your cat resembles a new pattern of wallpaper.
Binge eating. Your cat eats anything, from the Persian rug to your favorite Limburger cheese.
Lapsed hygiene. Your cat looks like he borrowed his filthy coat from a homeless man on the subway.

Aggressive behavior. Your cat bites the neighbor's Doberman.
Self-destructive behavior. Your cat plays "home on the range" while you're cooking.
Running away. Your cat calls 911 and bolts when the firemen chop down the door.

This chapter offers commentary on numerous stressful situations in the daily lives of contemporary cats. *Shiatsu* is appropriate whenever any of these symptoms develop.

THE CAT IS A LONELY HUNTER

The cat is a lonely hunter. Every day, while you are away for extended periods, your cat negotiates the stress of nothing to do with nobody else. Your cat's eyes may be glazed over from watching too many *Tom and Jerry* tapes on the VCR. Unsupervised cats have also been known to bankrupt their owners through unauthorized use of credit cards at mail order fishmongers.

Upon returning home, pet your cat underneath the chin and above the eyebrows to the forehead. Let your cat see that you have not abandoned the most precious creature in your life. If your cat has experienced excessive boredom in your absence, calm his mind by performing *shiatsu* under the chin and recite the cat poetry of T.S. Eliot.

I prefer not to be alone.

I prefer to live in the country.

THE MONSTER IN THE BOX

Among the pressures of city life for the once nomadic cat are the restrictions of living in crowded quarters. Stir crazy cats, however, are tackling the problem with entrepreneurial zeal, cashing in by licensing new fads to relieve stress, like "Vase Hockey," "Buzz the Landlord" and "View from the Ledge."

A touch of *shiatsu* will calm a keyed up cat. If your cat's muscles are tense along the spine, give them a light massage, stroking gently down both sides of the vertebrae with your fingertips or with a metal spoon handle. Gold or silver are the metals of choice to discharge static electricity. If you can play the spoons, serenade her with the following tunes: "The Green, Green Grass of Home" and "Born Free." Felines will purr along with you if the music strikes an harmonious chord.

IF ON A WINTER'S NIGHT A STRAY

If a stray approaches with pleading eyes and asks for a safe haven on a winter's night, consider the chaos that you might invite into your home. How will the kitty in residence respond? Reapportioning territory is work for diplomats, not philanthropists. Just say "no." Then bolt the door.

If you do, however, find the temptation irresistible, your survival will depend on your cunning. Massage the neck of each cat while the others are not looking. Let each one know they are dearest to you.

He who defends boundaries defends impermanence.

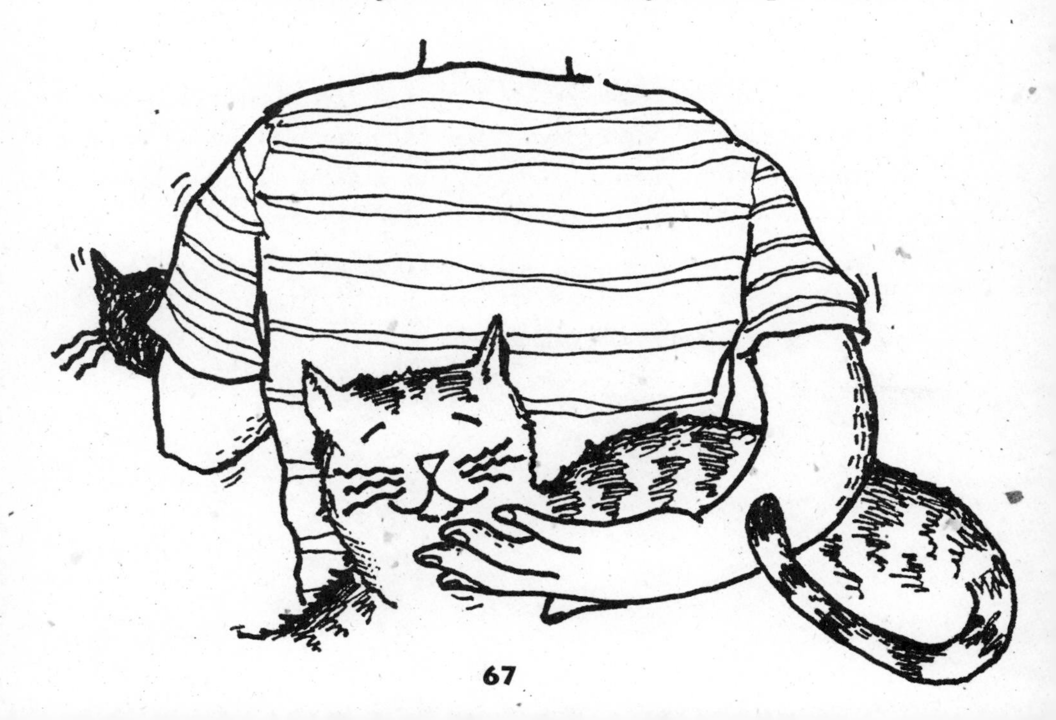

Try the *finger print technique*. Press your thumb on your cat's coat until you leave a deep impression. When you have taken the effort to brand your cat with your unique touch, your cat will feel more secure.

The projectile hurling of furballs is a stressful activity for cats, especially if the pitcher demonstrates a marked tendency for wildness. If your cat recognizes the strike zone, he will enjoy a long and healthy career in the cat's national pastime. After a game, cats enjoy sitting in a whirlpool and a session of *shiatsu*.

If your cat experiences muscle stiffness, try to invigorate *qi* through appropriate warm up exercises before pitching. Sometimes when cats feel sick, they often recover their health naturally by simply resting. Just hold your cat gently.

I like to stretch in the seventh inning.

NATURE WAITS

The regularity of cats is a vital matter of domestic security. Cat owners often worry about dyspeptic cats who look fatigued after long stretches of inactivity. Does your cat devour a neighbor's garden in search of fiber?

Massaging the *tsubos* along the midsection of the backbone is an excellent treatment for stomach ailments, including indigestion and constipation. In a circular motion, gently rub the rib cage of the constipated cat. Then lightly massage the abdomen. With wavelike pressure from head to the lower back, try to move things along.

He who laughs first has not been there.

If that fails to work, you might consider a non-*shiatsu* approach. Try offering coffee and a cigarette or a ride on the Cyclone at the amusement park.

HIGH FLYING CATS

Many people experience a fear of flying. When airborne, they feel a shortness of breath, and worse, the inadequacy of insurance coverage. But can you imagine a cat's fear of flying, buried in a crate in the cold baggage hold? It's no wonder that we read too many reports of cats escaping from their owners and scampering along airport runways.

During flight, provide herbal tea and *shiatsu* to limit the symptoms of travel sickness. Upon arrival at your destination, *shiatsu* will help reorient your cat to life out of prison by providing a balance of energy.

I do not fly. I leap.

RAGING CAT

Some cats respond to household stress with overly aggressive behavior. If your cat presents the following symptoms, he may be considering a boxing career:

When a hurricane comes, I hide under the bed.

1. Punches his way out of paper bags;
2. Shadow boxes to the center of the room every time a doorbell rings;
3. Taunts other cats during local stalk, pounce and catch competitions.

Do not touch a cat looking for a fight. Try to empathize to soothe bottled up emotions. Once you have worn out the combatant with a deft discussion of the merits of *shiatsu*, he will take a relaxing fall.

THANKSGIVING IS DAY FROM HELL

Most cats hate Thanksgiving. Cats generally fear guests, and more guests arrive on Thanksgiving than any other day. Many cats will hide for 24-hour stretches on high shelves or in closets rather than face the invading hordes. How does your cat cope with the noise of silver on china, the couch crowded with uninviting laps, and the uncomfortable delays when access to the litter box is blocked? Can the scraps of turkey and giblets left under the table help compensate for frisky boys?

To overcome guest stress on holidays, don't celebrate at your house. Visit the in-laws and hire a cat sitter who practices *shiatsu*.

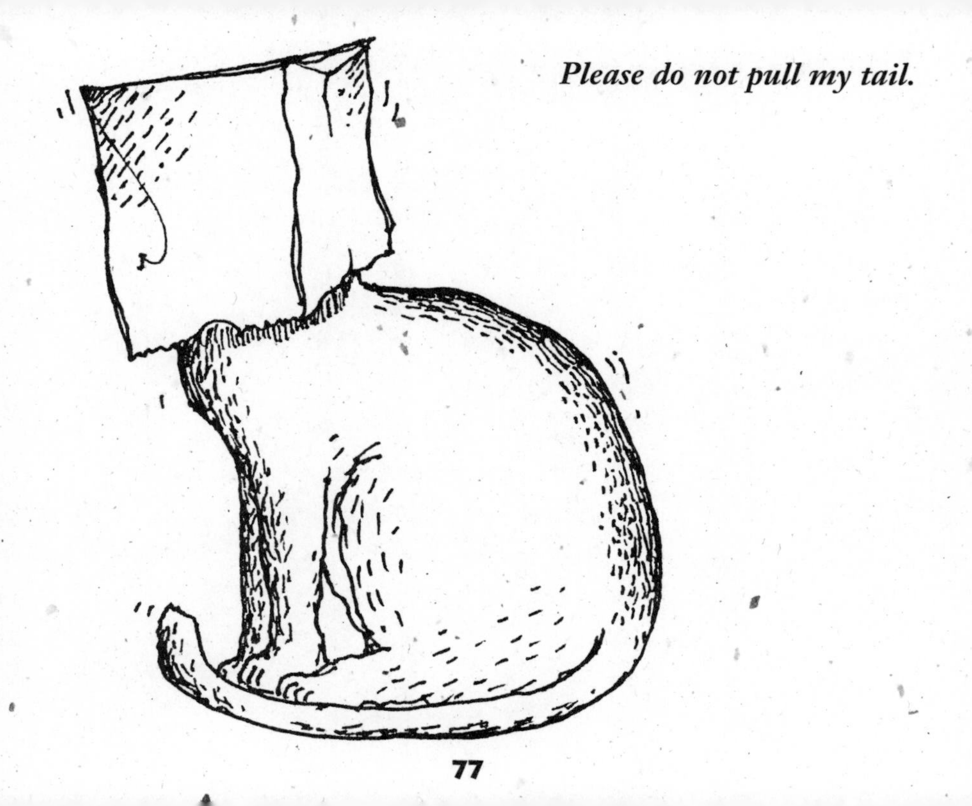

Please do not pull my tail.

SOME ENCHANTED EVENING

There are many potential dangers in the modern household that may lead to excessive stress for cats. Some enchanted evening, your cat may meet a vacuum cleaner across a crowded room. Other worrisome objects include irons, refrigerators and microwave ovens. If your cat meets a menacing stranger in paradise, see if immediate medical attention is required.

Your cat may develop a phobia to household appliances. The most common symptom is for your cat to experience heart palpitations anytime he hears the hum of a motor. Watch for breathlessness. Relieve anxiety with a loving hug and a gentle dose of *shiatsu*. Try *shiatsu* to the ears and outfitting your cat with earplugs.

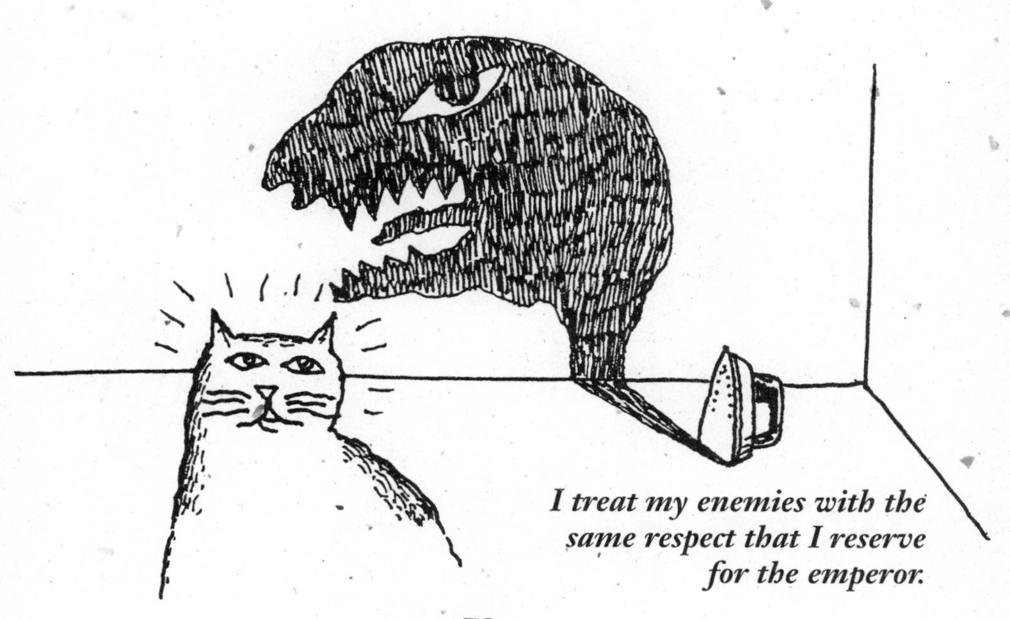

I treat my enemies with the same respect that I reserve for the emperor.

Chapter IV
Case Studies: From the Nine-Life Cycle

It is no longer enough to teach cats to stay off train tracks to ensure that they lead healthy and rewarding lives. Cats are flocking to holistic practitioners who provide preventative cat-care. Several full-service cat maintenance organizations (CMO's) now specialize in *shiatsu*.

On the following pages are case studies of cats at critical moments in their lives when *shiatsu* has played an important role.

MISHA, THE NAUGHTY KITTEN

Misha, a ginger tabby with a freckled nose who was born in the year of the rat—a good sign for a cat—could not follow the hectic training agenda that his mother had scheduled for the entire litter of six. (One particular morning's rigorous schedule included the following activities: advanced biting technique, the nape bite, snapping the spine of a mouse, the box step for litter box, and climbing the low branch on the apple tree.)

YES!
?

At five weeks old, Misha would suddenly fall asleep whenever it was his turn to practice. He said he was sorry and wanted to continue through his paces, but that didn't stop his mother from being very angry. She seemed to resent the time Misha spent receiving *shiatsu* treatments. She wondered whether it was the *shiatsu* that was making Misha too relaxed to carry on his schooling.

Misha learned to stay awake when his owner applied the *scout's oath technique* for acupressure. Holding up his index, middle and ring fingers he lightly stroked along Misha's energy *meridian*s to introduce him early to the joy of *shiatsu*. He avoided applying strong pressure, since young cats have an abundance of *qi*.

FIELD OF DREAMS

Valerie lived on a 60-acre farm outside of Des Moines, Iowa. She had a pedigree, having been born from the union of two Russian show cats. She was a stunning beauty with a thick, glossy red coat, a lithe body and bright blue eyes.

At a year old, after going through her first heat, male cats were beginning to notice her. She heard crude whistles on the street when her owners took her to the veterinarian in town.

With the overpopulation of cats that has led to the killing of millions of unwanted, healthy pets each year in American cities, her owners considered having Valerie spayed. But they felt that a purebred should continue a distinguished line. Furthermore, they had room on the farm for an expansive litter. Their two boys, aged twelve and nine, were poised to take on new responsibilities.

The owners gave both Valerie and her "beau to be" *shiatsu* on a regular basis in the days prior to the mating. (It is very common for inexperienced cats to have trouble completing the necessary acts if they are nervous and frightened, and *shiatsu* improves the libido. This is a fertile area for future research.) *Shiatsu* to *tsubo*s along the lower back heightens sexual energy.

An unorthodox *shiatsu* technique that is most effective in preparing cats for mating is *the benediction*. With the index and middle finger raised like those of a priest at mass, the owner applied physical and spiritual pressure on the *tsubo*s of the heart, thus blessing the union.

The treatment was so successful, Valerie demanded *shiatsu* during her gestation and the hours prior to delivery. She gave birth to a splendid litter of eight kittens.

HENRY'S MID-LIFE CRISIS

Henry, a middle-aged Russian blue, had been feeling blue. He lost his appetite and had bouts of insomnia. For Henry, the thrill was gone.

To help Henry feel the pulse of life again, his owner wanted to take him to the beautician to give him the latest furstyle. The owner also planned to teach him the four-foot mambo and new sports like fence hopping.

Henry's poor behavior, however, was finally traced to the day that he had stopped receiving his daily *shiatsu*. Once *shiatsu* was reintroduced, Henry rediscovered his zest for life.

JULES, IN MOURNING

For seven years, Jules, a purebred Abyssian, and Jim, a tabby, shared an apartment on the Upper East Side of Manhattan. They hated each other. Jules was a patrician cat, born with a silver mouse rattle in his dish. Jim was a proletarian who spent his kittenhood in a lunch box.

They would have fierce arguments during the daily talk shows on the radio. Jules wanted a leash law to keep the riffraff off the streets. Jim, however, insisted that denial of access to parks was unconstitutional for cats. A talented mimic, Jim would entertain at the raucous parties in Late Nite Alley, mocking the sour-faces of Jules when the butler served canapés with liver instead of anchovies.

One day, without warning, Jim had a fatal heart attack. Jules, in mourning, suffered a period of major depression. His owners gave him *shiatsu* to perk him up. This treatment finally helped Jules to arise to face the day after two weeks in bed. But an unexpected behavioral change suddenly affected Jules who began to think that he was Jim. He suddenly relished liver for dinner and stopped using a napkin. This astonishing leap of the soul lasted for a few months.

At fourteen years old, Jules was also beginning to suffer the chronic physical indignities of aged cats. His joints were stiff with arthritis and after a recent hearing loss, he meowed louder than ever.

Jules underwent a regular *shiatsu* program at a senior citizen center to help him enjoy his golden years. The seniors who treated him knew that by providing gentle *shiatsu* for an elderly cat, they would increase his vitality and healing power. But they were surprised to find that the petting was a calming influence that lowered their own blood pressure. They also noted improvement in the digital dexterity that they require for bingo and shuffleboard.

Jules enjoyed the gentle contact with the seniors, though he often complained that the rooms were generally too warm.

More shiatsu, please.